This edition published by Parragon Books Ltd in 2015

Parragon Books Ltd
Chartist House
15–17 Trim Street
Bath BA1 1HA, UK
www.parragon.com

ISBN 978-1-4723-9704-1

Printed in China

MARVEL
COLLECTION

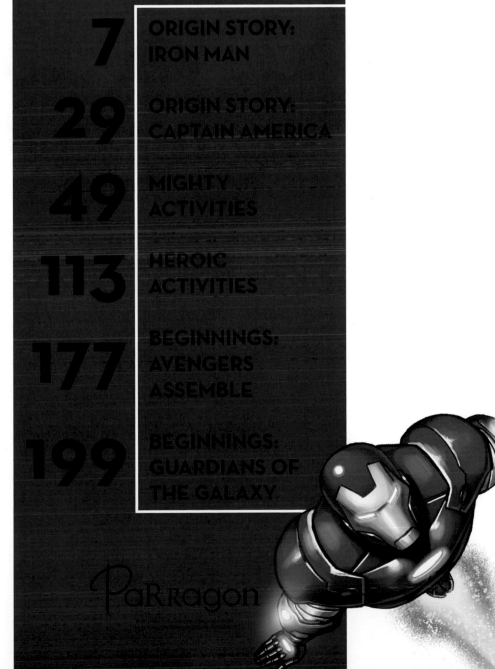

PaRragon

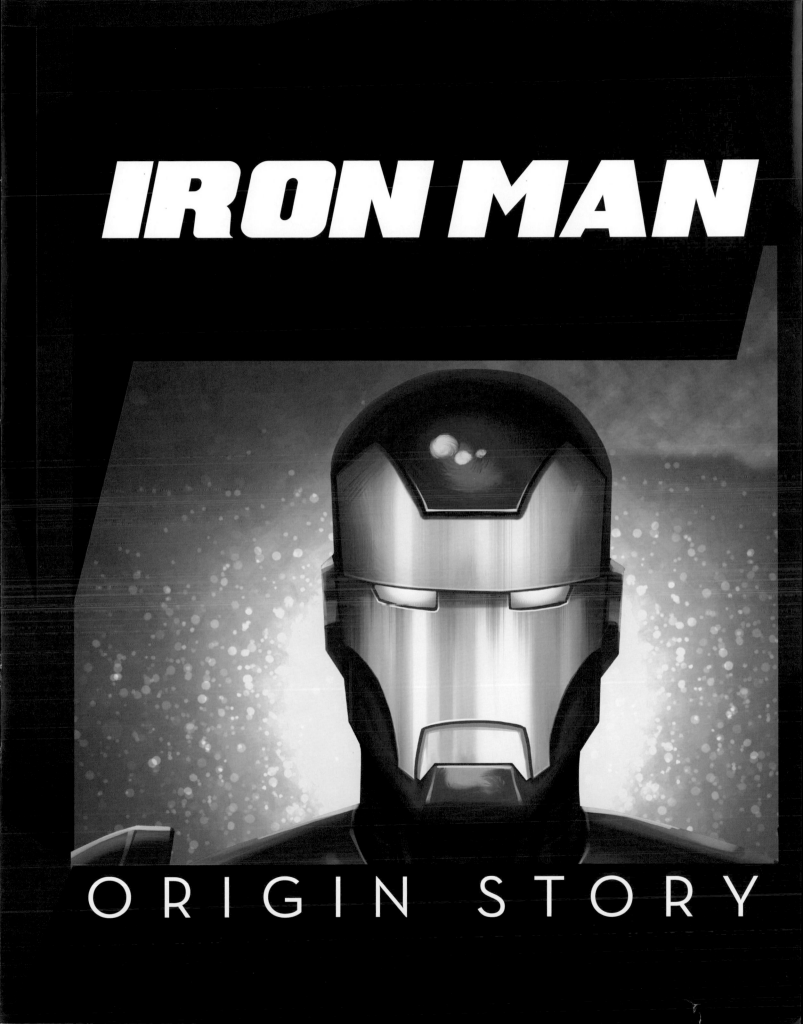

This is Tony Stark. Tony is usually a normal guy – only with a lot more money. But when Tony puts on his special armour, he becomes more powerful than most other people. He even has a different name. When Tony puts on his armour, he becomes ...

... the Invincible Iron Man!

Tony wasn't born a super hero. He hasn't always fought to protect people. But with villains on the loose, like Titanium Man and Iron Monger – who use Tony's technology for their own, evil purposes – Tony feels it is his responsibility to stop them.

Tony didn't always get the job done this easily. Or this well. Tony's armour wasn't always so sleek. In fact, when he first became Iron Man, Tony's armour didn't even shine!

But if you really want to know how Iron Man was born, we need to start with the man behind the mask. We need to start with Tony.

Tony had so much money that he could go anywhere he wanted.

He loved to have fun. And he loved the finer things in life.

But Tony also worked hard. He was a brilliant inventor and he knew all sorts of things about science.

He loved to work with magnetic fields. Using them, he created a powerful energy force that he called 'repulsor technology'.

The military was interested in Tony's work. In fact, it was in a secret army lab that Tony's life was changed forever. An enemy army attacked and Tony was badly hurt!

Since Tony was famous, he was recognized straight away. The enemy knew all about his inventions. They tossed him in a prison room filled with electronic and mechanical equipment. They wanted him to create a mighty weapon for them.

To make things worse, they told Tony that his heart had been hurt in the blast. He didn't have much longer to live.

Tony soon found he was not alone in the cell. The enemy had captured another famous scientist – Professor Yinsen. The enemy wanted the two men to work together on the great weapon.

But Professor Yinsen had other ideas – he knew a way to keep Tony alive!

The two men worked tirelessly to create something that would save Tony's life and, at the same time, help them to escape the prison.

Finally, the men completed the device that Tony would always need to wear on his chest, in order to keep his heart beating. But that wasn't all they had created.

Using Tony's repulsor technology, they had built boots that could help a man fly!

Gloves that could crush steel!

And a helmet that could protect a man from the most terrible blast!

Tony put on the armour and proved that no walls could hold ...

... the Iron Man! It wasn't long before the enemy realized they were fighting a losing battle.

After he had escaped from prison and saved Professor Yinsen, Tony flew home. But almost as soon as he got there, he realized that he could now help where others couldn't. He was strong, unstoppable and frightening.

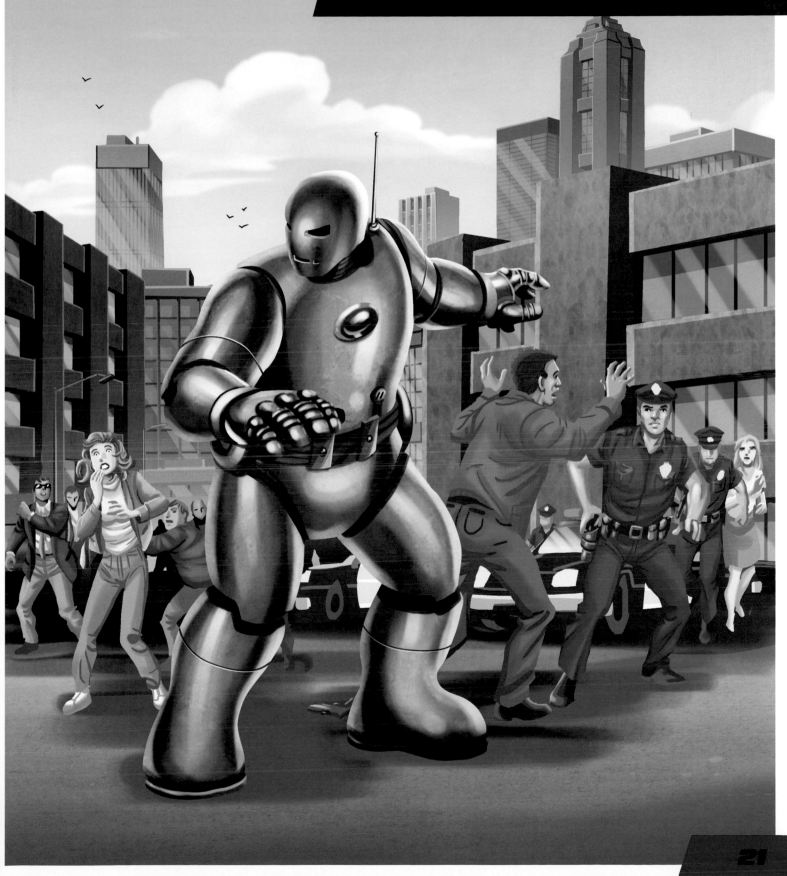

But maybe he was a little too frightening. Tony didn't want innocent people to be scared of him. He decided the suit needed to change.

Tony thought that Iron Man needed something as smooth and stylish as he was. He needed to create a lighter suit.

Although his chest plate couldn't change,
everything around it could.
Soon, Tony perfected the armour ...

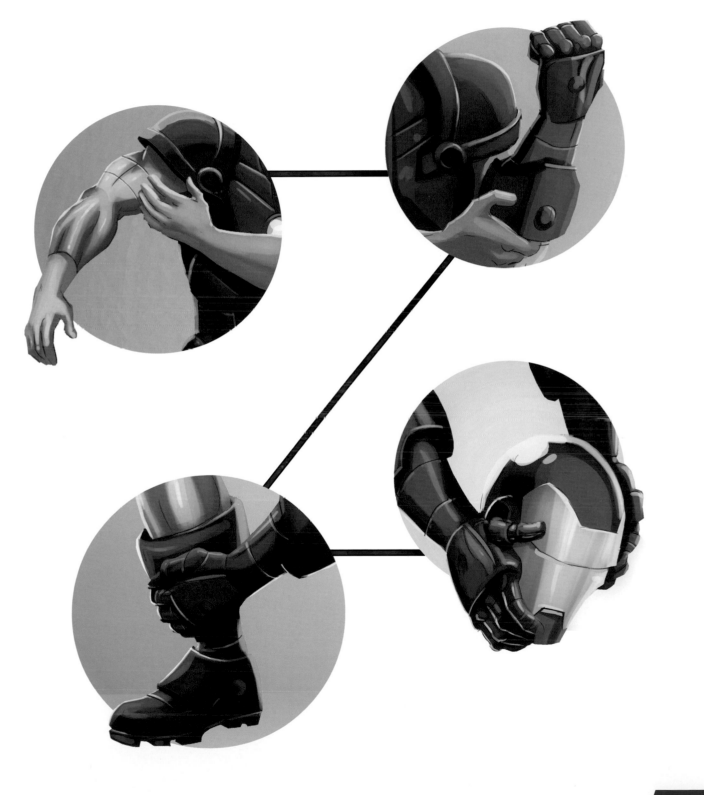

And as Iron Man, Tony never stops fighting. He protects people at home and around the world.

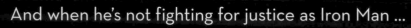

And when he's not fighting for justice as Iron Man ...

... Tony runs his company, Stark Industries.

Stark Industries might need Tony to be a businessman, but with new villains attacking every day, the world needs Tony to be ...

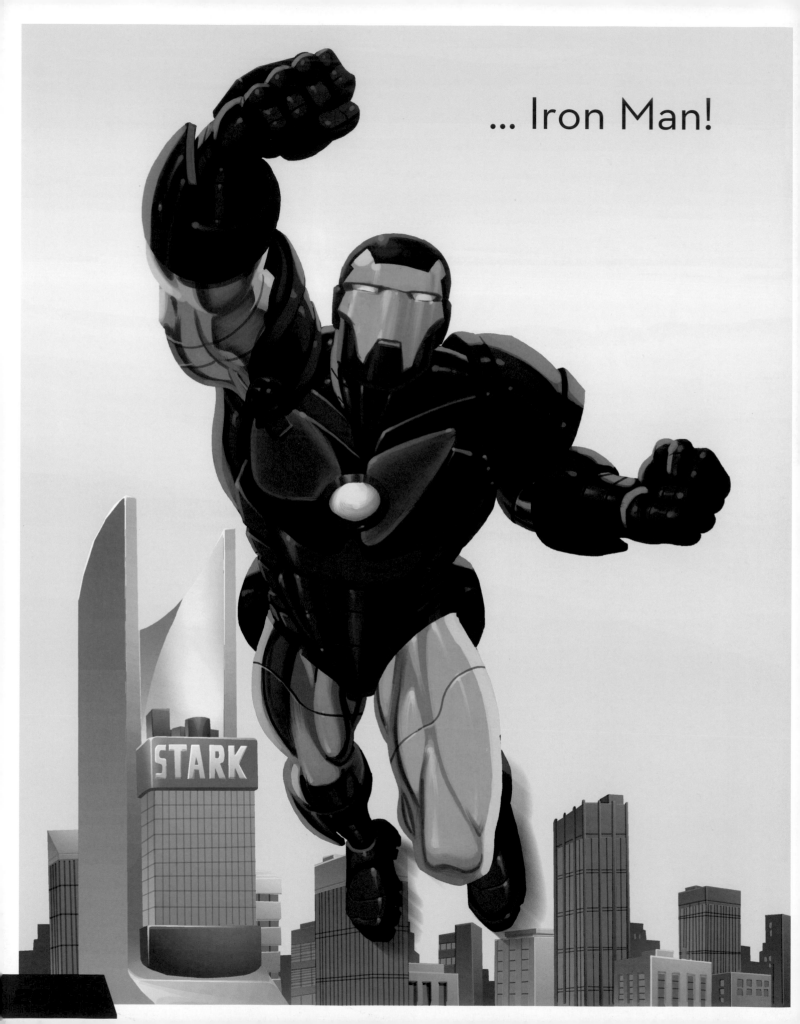

CAPTAIN AMERICA

ORIGIN STORY

Long ago, a peaceful little island sat just off the mainland of a place that was called different things by all the different nations of people who lived there.

As time went on, more and more people came to this little island.

They wanted to leave behind the lives they led in a place they called the Old World, and build new ones in a place where they believed anything was possible.

For most, this island was the first stop on the path to a new life in this young nation.

This island was known as Manhattan, in the city of New York.
And the country would become known as the United States of America –
or America, for short.

Before America was even 200 years old, it was called upon to fight alongside other countries in a terrible war that was destroying the world.

The news of war moved people. It seemed like everyone in the country wanted to join the army to help.

Including a young man named Steve Rogers.

Steve had been upset about the war for some time. Now that America was involved, he could do something about it.

Soon, Steve was in a long queue of men waiting to be examined. If the men passed their medical, they would be sent to join the army.

Steve waited his turn.

Every man so far had passed.

Steve was confident he would, too.

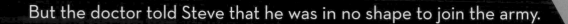
But the doctor told Steve that he was in no shape to join the army.

Then he told Steve there was another way to get into the army. He handed Steve a file marked:

Classified – Project: Rebirth.

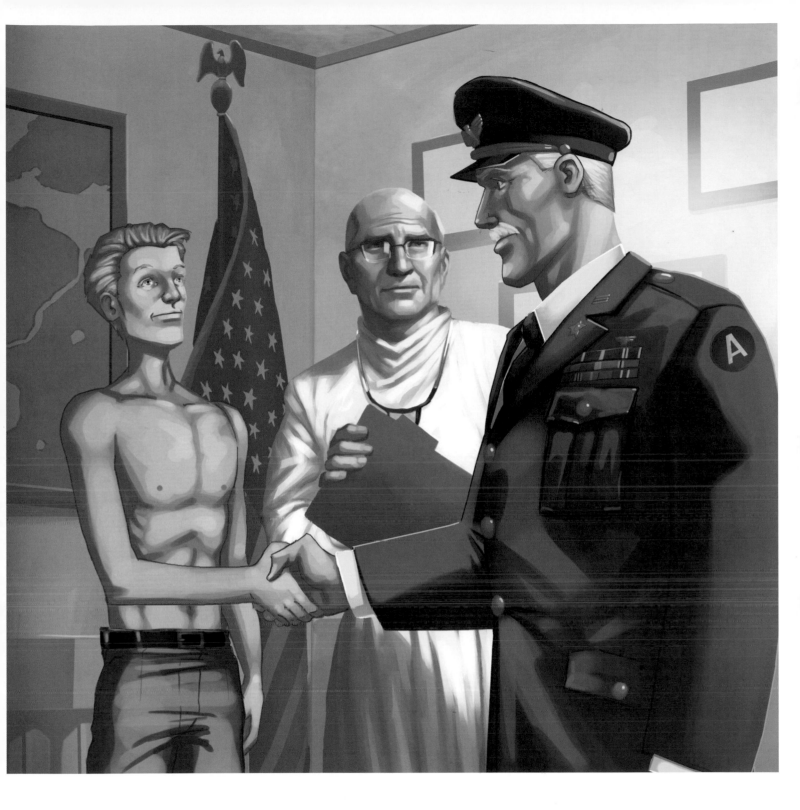

The doctor told Steve that if the experiment worked,
he would be able to join the army after all.
Steve said he would try anything to become a soldier.
The doctor called in a general named Chester Phillips.
The General was in charge of Project: Rebirth.

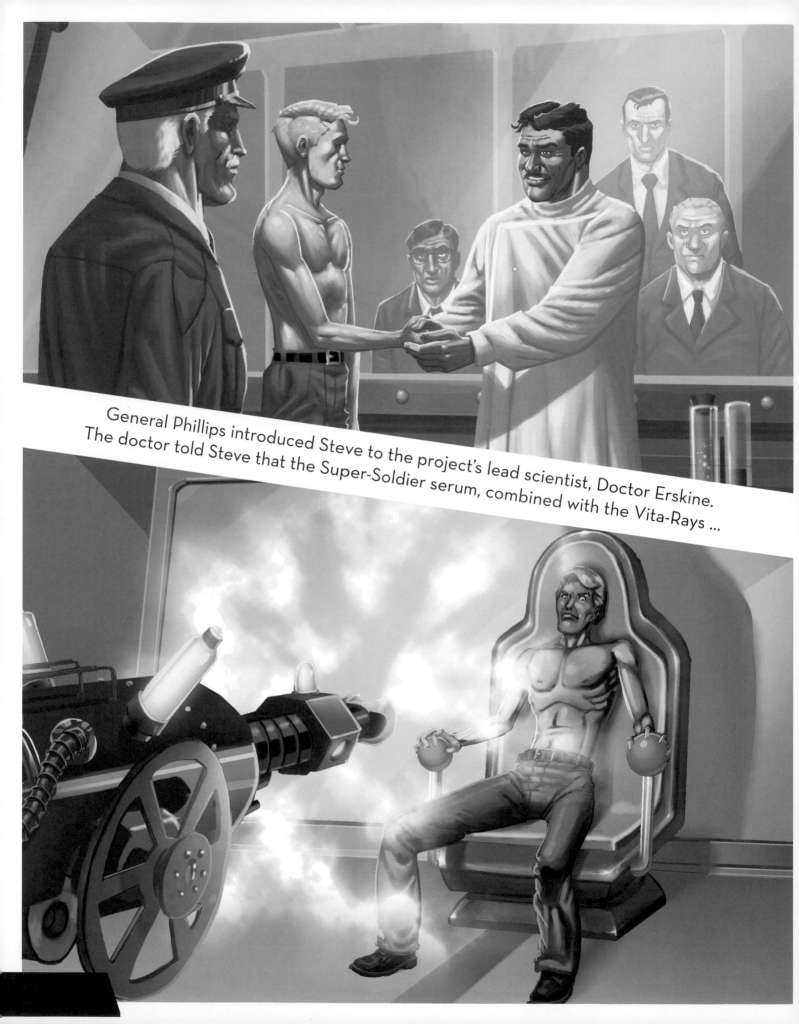

General Phillips introduced Steve to the project's lead scientist, Doctor Erskine. The doctor told Steve that the Super-Soldier serum, combined with the Vita-Rays ...

... would transform him from frail and sickly into America's FIRST AVENGER!

The experiment was a SUCCESS!

But before Steve, General Phillips or anyone else in the lab could notice, an enemy spy who had been working in the lab suddenly attacked! He did not want the Americans to have such power! The doctor was hurt and unable to duplicate the serum.

But Steve, in his new Super-Soldier body, was safe. The army put Steve through a very special training camp to teach him how to use his new body.

The general presented Steve with a special shield made of the strongest metal known and a unique costume to help Steve mask his identity.

With the costume and shield, Steve would now be known as America's most powerful soldier ...

Captain America!

Captain America's missions were often dangerous. In order to keep his secret safe, the general asked Steve to pretend to be a clumsy army private.

But when no one was looking, Steve donned his costume and fought for justice.

Steve's reputation as a clumsy guy meant he was often transferred between units. But Steve's moving around allowed Captain America to fight on many different fronts of the worldwide war!

No one ever suspected that the worst private in the US Army was also the best soldier that the army had!

Captain America kept on fighting for liberty, until finally ... the war was won.

Though the country might not always live up to its promises, as long as Steve was able, he vowed to protect America and its ideals: justice, equality, freedom ...

... and the dream of what the nation he loved could accomplish.

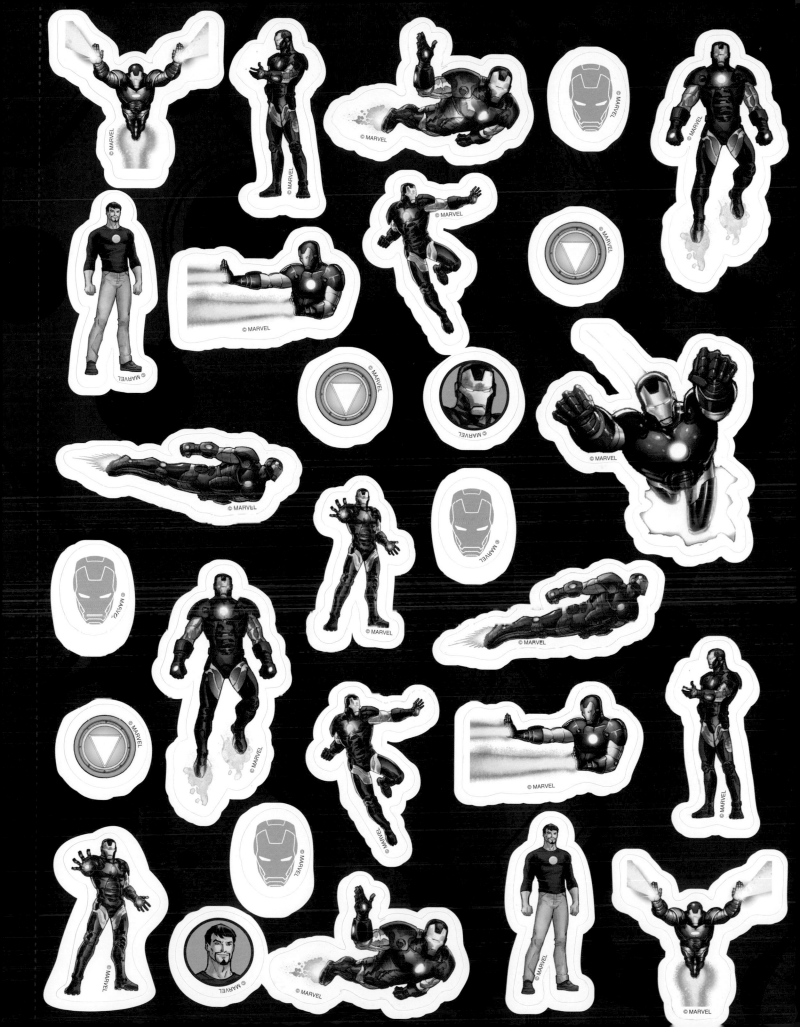

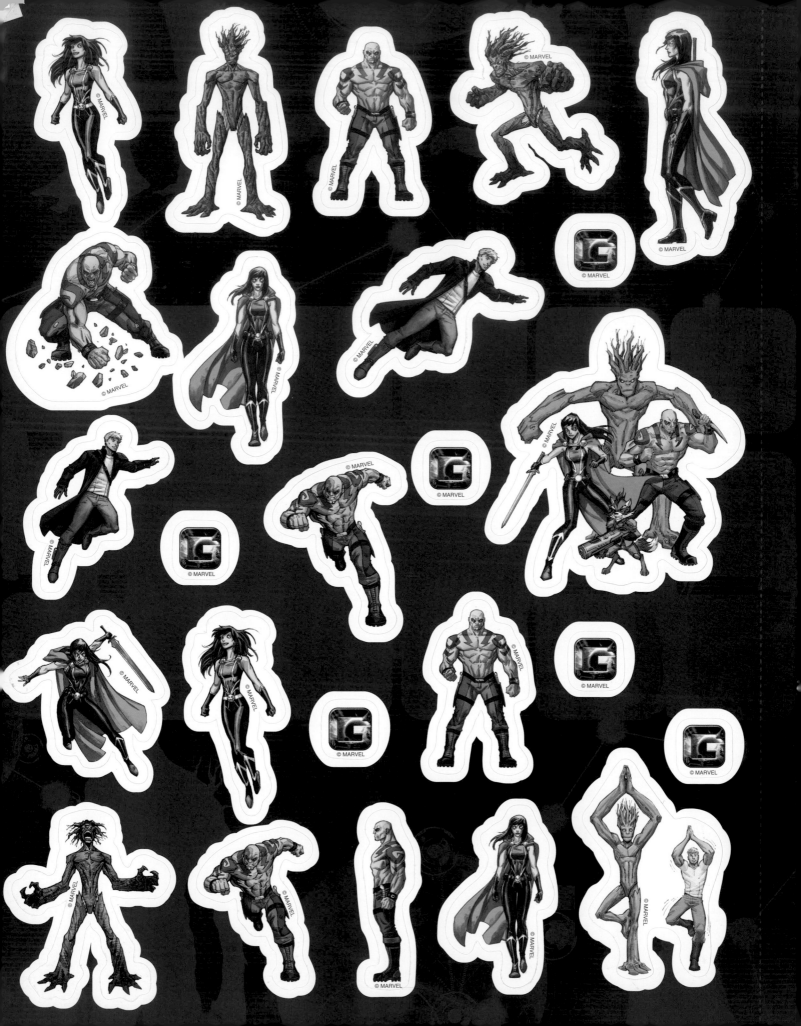

AVENGERS ASSEMBLE

MIGHTY ACTIVITIES

Colour and complete these awesome activities! Then find the answers on page 112.

The Falcon is heading to work ...

Falcon needs to know his team. Draw a line to match each Avenger to their name.

Captain America

Hulk

Thor

Iron Man

Black Widow

Hawkeye

Answers on page 112

Suddenly, there's an explosion! The Avengers will have to wait.

HYDRA is attacking!

The villain emerges. Unscramble the letters below to find out who it is.

K.D.O.O.M.

The villain is __ . __ . __ . __ . __ .

Answer on page 112

Falcon is outnumbered!

56

The HYDRA agents are shielding M.O.D.O.K. from Falcon's view. Can you spot him?

Answer on page 112

M.O.D.O.K. retreats to the sewers.

M.O.D.O.K. is trying to lose Falcon in the sewer tunnels. Find a way through the maze to help Falcon catch the evil genius.

FINISH

START

Answer on page 112

Good job! Falcon has the villain cornered.

M.O.D.O.K. uses his energy projector to disable Falcon's suit.

His suit finally working again, Falcon flies off to join the Avengers.

Can you find these Avengers words in the grid below? Remember to look up, down, forwards, backwards and diagonally.

AMERICA	BLACK WIDOW
CAPTAIN	FALCON
HAWKEYE	HULK
IRON MAN	NICK FURY
SHIELD	THOR

F	Y	D	L	E	I	H	S	W	T
R	R	R	M	Y	Y	E	N	O	P
N	U	O	X	P	K	Q	O	D	N
I	F	H	A	L	F	A	C	I	A
A	K	T	U	M	M	G	L	W	M
T	C	H	U	E	X	G	A	K	N
P	I	D	R	L	B	E	F	C	O
A	N	I	V	J	G	P	F	A	R
C	C	N	K	L	S	C	F	L	I
A	H	A	W	K	E	Y	E	B	B

I hope the Avengers don't mind that I'm a little late, thinks Falcon.

The Avengers work with Nick Fury and his government agency, S.H.I.E.L.D. Fill in the blank to discover what S.H.I.E.L.D. stands for. There are four options for you to choose from.

Strategic
Homeland
Intervention
Enforcement
L_____
Division

| Laser-fighting |
| Logistics |
| Label-making |
| Logic-enhanced |

Answer on page 112

"You've all been given your locations, Avengers," Fury says as Falcon approaches. "Pair up and head out."

Falcon has a question for Nick Fury. To work out what it is, cross out every other letter of this sequence, then transfer the remaining letters to the spaces below.
The first one has been done for you.

ΙWOHBAATE ITSE TOHAE DEOMIERRAGIECNACNYB?

W _ _ _   _ _   _ _ _   _ _ _ _ _ _ _ _ _

"There is no emergency. It's your training day," Fury tells Falcon.

Falcon heads to the Statue of Liberty for the first part of his training.
Can you spot the two Avengers waiting for him there?

Which path should Falcon follow to catch up with Thor?

Falcon should take path ____.

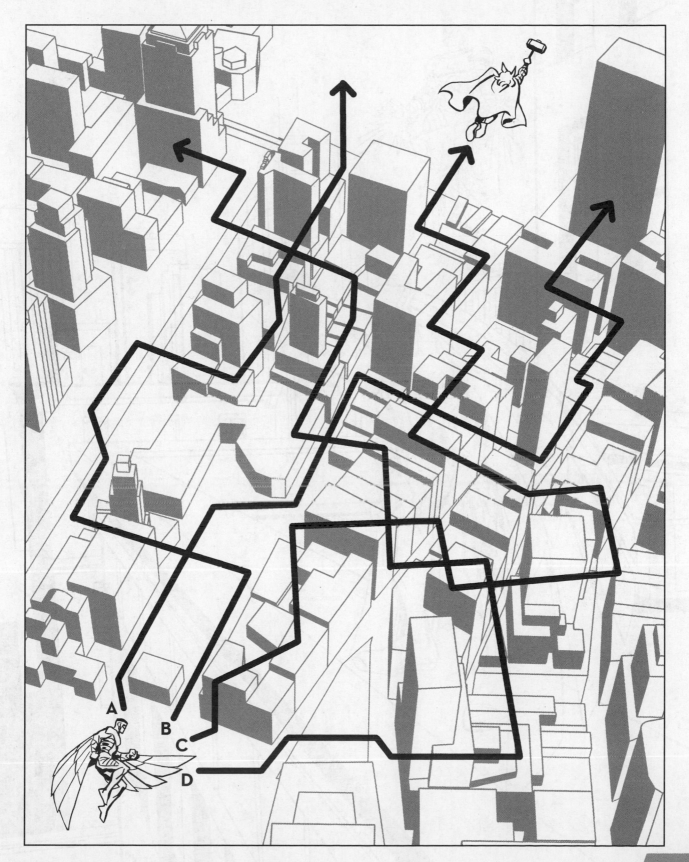

The newest Avenger can't keep up with the God of Thunder.

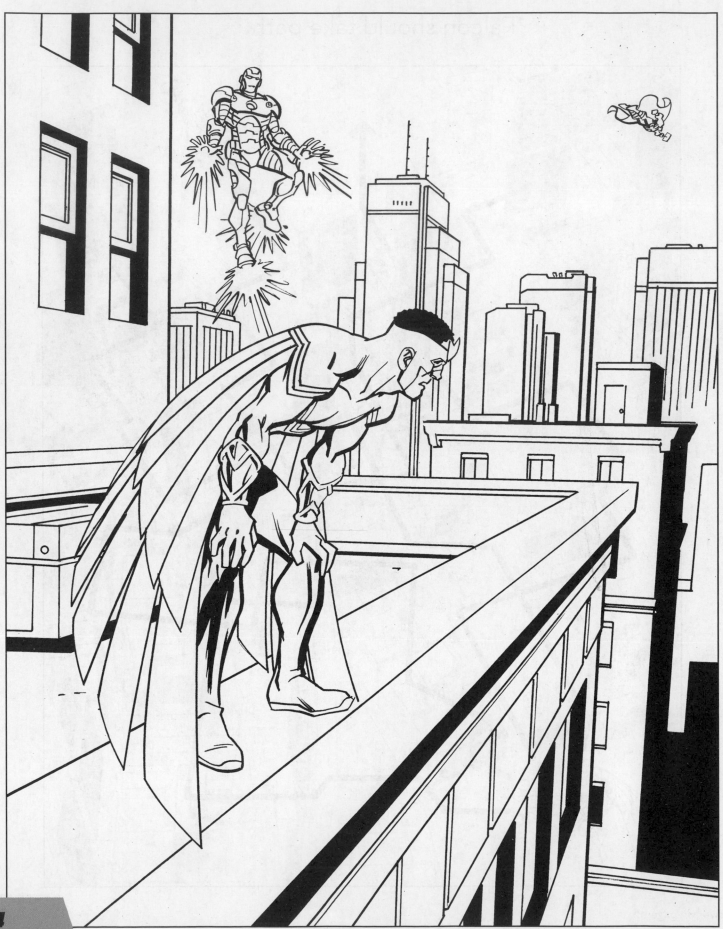

"If you can't beat your opponent at his own game, change the game altogether," Iron Man tells Falcon.

Which of these powers does Iron Man's armour **not** have?

Answer: _____

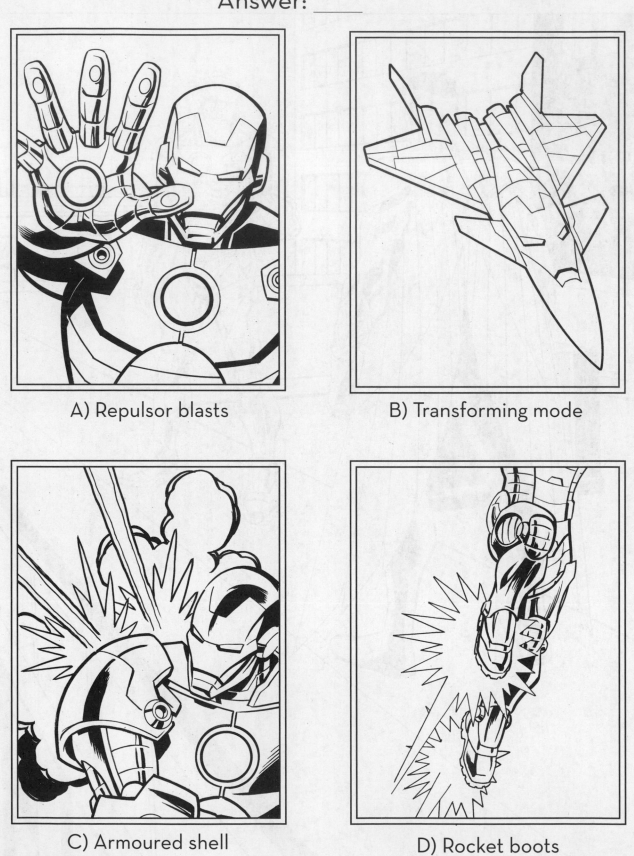

A) Repulsor blasts

B) Transforming mode

C) Armoured shell

D) Rocket boots

Answer on page 112

Iron Man and Falcon race through the woods. But the Armoured Avenger is too fast for Falcon.

"Time to change the game," says Falcon, releasing flechettes from his hard-light wings.

Falcon's flechettes explode on impact.

Which of these powers does Falcon not possess?

Answer: ____

A) Falcon cry

B) Retractable talons

C) Exploding flechettes

D) Hard-light wings

Answer on page 112

Falcon has to fly to his next test. Which route on the map will take him to his second challenge?

Route ___ will lead Falcon to his next challenge.

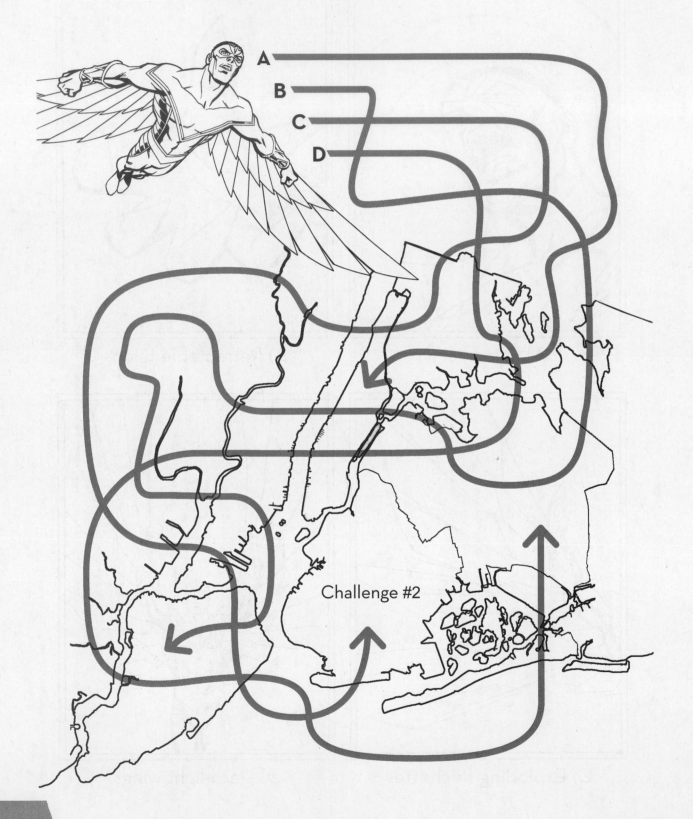

Answer on page 112

The route leads Falcon to an abandoned construction site. He is immediately under attack!

Which of these is Captain America's real shield?

Answer on page 11

But Cap was just trying to get Falcon's attention. Join the dots to see who Falcon's second challenge really is.

The battle begins! Draw the missing scene.

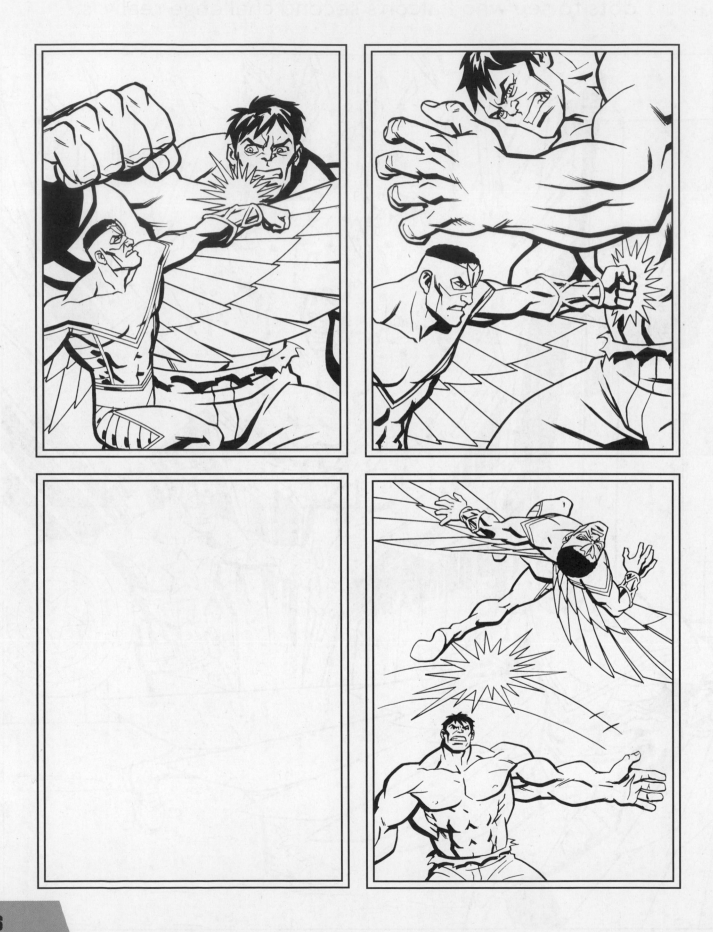

Falcon escapes to higher ground – and nearly flies into Cap!
"If you can't beat your opponent with brute force,
look to your other strengths," says the First Avenger.

Hulk catches up with Falcon and corners him.

But the Jade Giant is standing in wet cement and starts to sink!

Falcon and Captain America throw ropes to Hulk.
But which rope will help him climb out of the cement?

Answer on page 112

Can you match each hero to their symbol?

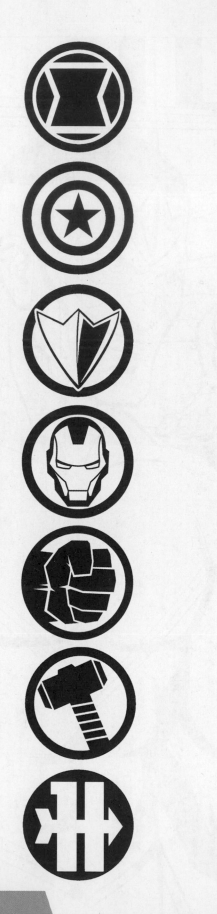

Answers on page 112

Falcon arrives at his final test in New York City.

"Black Widow is hiding somewhere in Times Square. All you have to do is find her and bring her in," Hawkeye tells Falcon.

Can you spot Black Widow on the street below?
Circle her when you find her.

Answer on page 112

"You just have to remember to take your time," Hawkeye tells the new Avenger. "Look for the person who doesn't want to be spotted."

But Black Widow won't go down without a fight!
Draw the missing battle scene.

"Mission accomplished," Black Widow says, shaking Falcon's hand. "Head back to S.H.I.E.L.D. and report in."

But on the way to Avengers Tower, Falcon notices a new threat. Join the dots to see what's causing the panic.

Time to change the game, thinks Falcon as he swoops into the fray.

Falcon needs to get the robot out of the city. The Avenger sets off small explosions to get the robot's attention. Connect the explosions to create a path for the villain to follow.

The robot is too powerful for Falcon. *Better use brains over brawn*, Falcon says to himself.

Where should Falcon fire his hard-light feather?
Choose the path that will knock the bridge down.

Splash! The robot falls into the deep water. With the enemy defeated, Falcon flies away to find out who was controlling it.

Can you help Falcon find the villain that doesn't want to be found? Circle the bad guy.

Answer on page 112

Falcon releases his flechettes. M.O.D.O.K.'s reign of terror is about to end.

KABOOM!! M.O.D.O.K. is offline!

Now the real battle begins!

Answers

Page 52:

Captain America
Hulk
Thor
Iron Man
Black Widow
Hawkeye

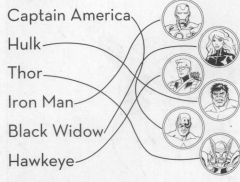

Page 55: The villain is M.O.D.O.K.

Page 57:

Page 60:

Page 65:

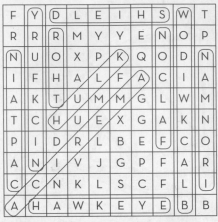

Page 67: Logistics

Page 69: WHAT IS THE EMERGENCY?

Page 71:

Page 73: Falcon should take path C.

Page 76: B

Page 81: A

Page 82: Route C will lead Falcon to his next challenge.

Page 84: A

Page 90: E

Page 92:

Page 95:

Page 105: D

Page 107:

AVENGERS ASSEMBLE

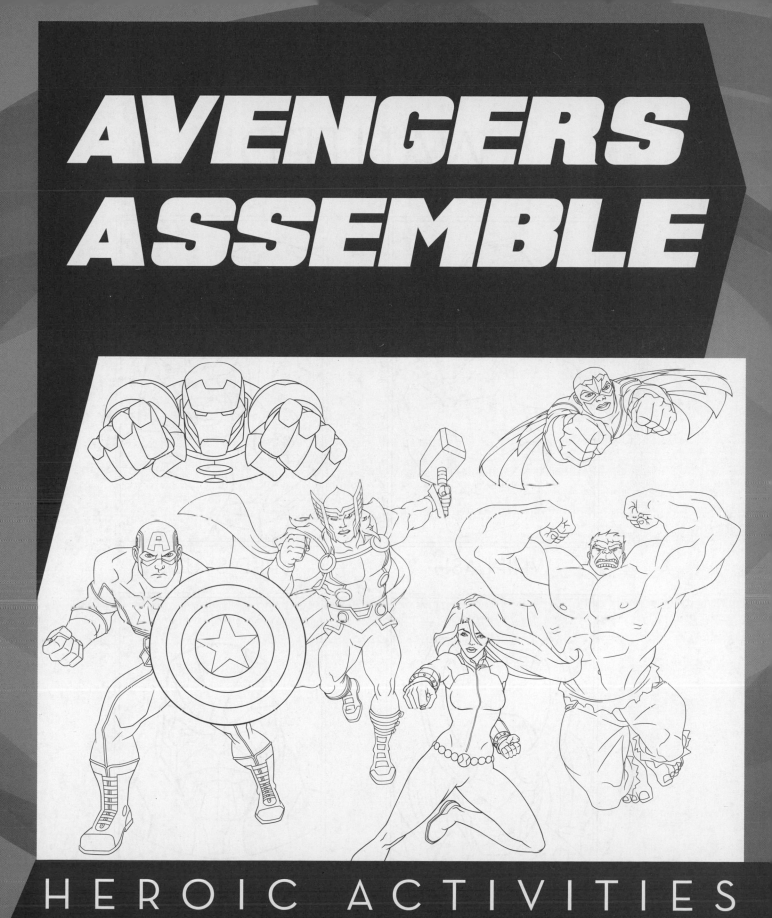

HEROIC ACTIVITIES

Colour and complete these super activities! Then find the answers on page 176.

Earth's Mightiest Heroes have a lot of enemies.
Colour in this poster of the villains.

WANTED!

WHIPLASH

RED SKULL

LOKI

THANOS

Unscramble the names of the Avengers' sinister foes.

1. KLOI

_____

2. ROTLUN

_____

3. ASHONT

_____

4. DHYAR

_____

5. DRE LKLUS

____ _____

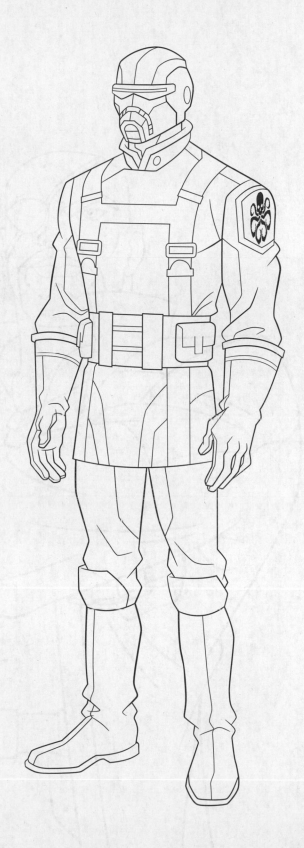

Answers on page 176

The Avengers work with Nick Fury and his government agency known as S.H.I.E.L.D.

"Loki is gaining on us. Time to call in the Avengers!"

"Time to suit up," says Iron Man.

Captain America needs to report in. Find the path that will lead him to S.H.I.E.L.D. headquarters.

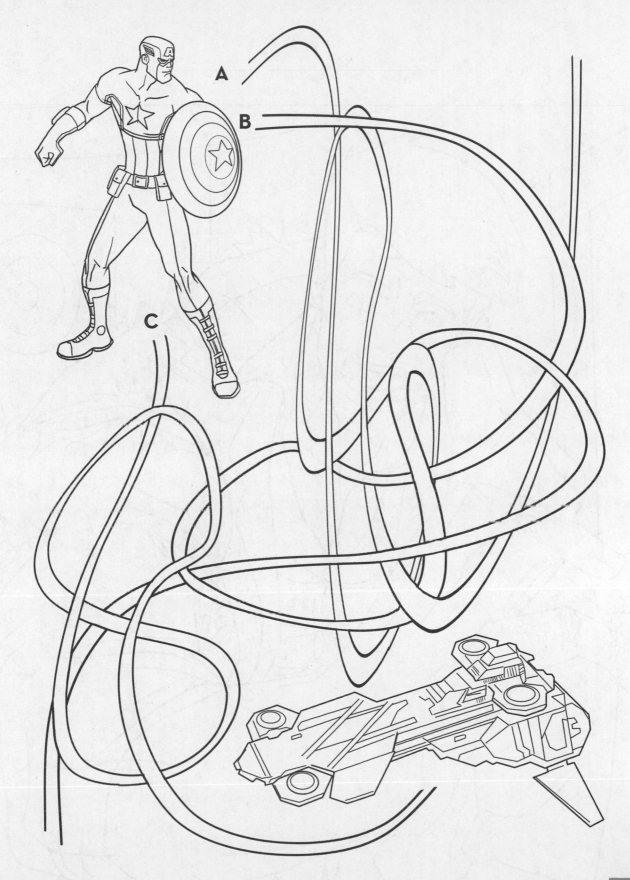

Dr Banner knows he has to help the Avengers.
Who does he change into?

_____

120

Answer on page 17

"Loki has hacked into S.H.I.E.L.D.'s defence systems and stolen a top-secret weapon!" Fury tells the Avengers.

Loki is the God of Mischief.

Loki has a brother. Can you guess who it is?
Complete this picture to find out!

Loki's brother is _____

Answer on page 176

Thor soon catches up with Loki.
"Looks like we're keeping this in the family!" he yells.

CRASH! The brothers battle until ...

... Loki ends up behind bars, where he belongs.

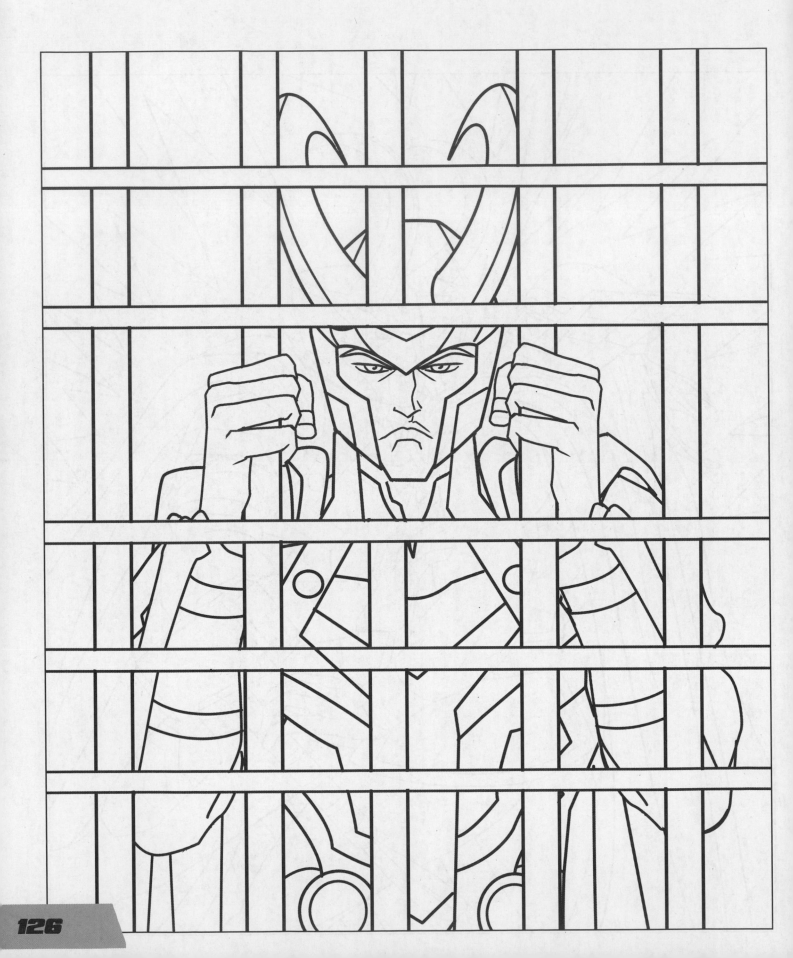

Loki is no match for the God of Thunder.

Which of these shadows belongs to Thor?
Write your answer below.

Shadow _____ belongs to Thor.

Answer on page 176

How well do you know the Avengers?
Draw a line to match each Super Hero to their real name.

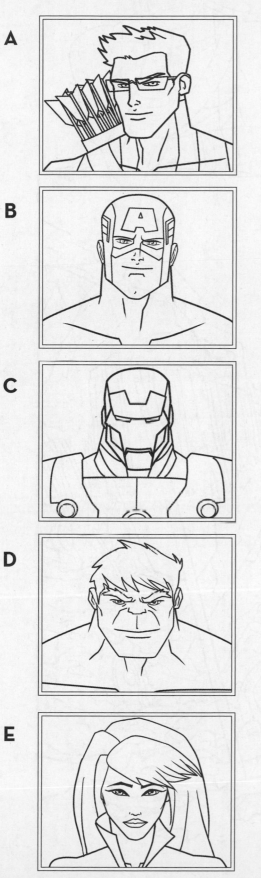

A

B

C

D

E

1. Natasha Romanoff

2. Clint Barton

3. Tony Stark

4. Steve Rogers

5. Bruce Banner

Answers on page 176

Hawkeye has dropped his arrows.
Can you help him find all five
so he can begin his training?

Answers on page 176

Black Widow is one of S.H.I.E.L.D.'s best super spies. Use your spy training to help her work out which of these statements is false.

A. Hulk is green.
B. Thor is from Asgard.
C. Falcon is Hawkeye's brother.
D. Nick Fury is the head of S.H.I.E.L.D.

Answer on page 176

Watch out! An evil enemy is after Hawkeye. He tries to defend himself, but is captured and taken away.

Black Widow is already in pursuit! Can you help her get to the plane to find Hawkeye? Find a route up the steps to the top of the cliff.

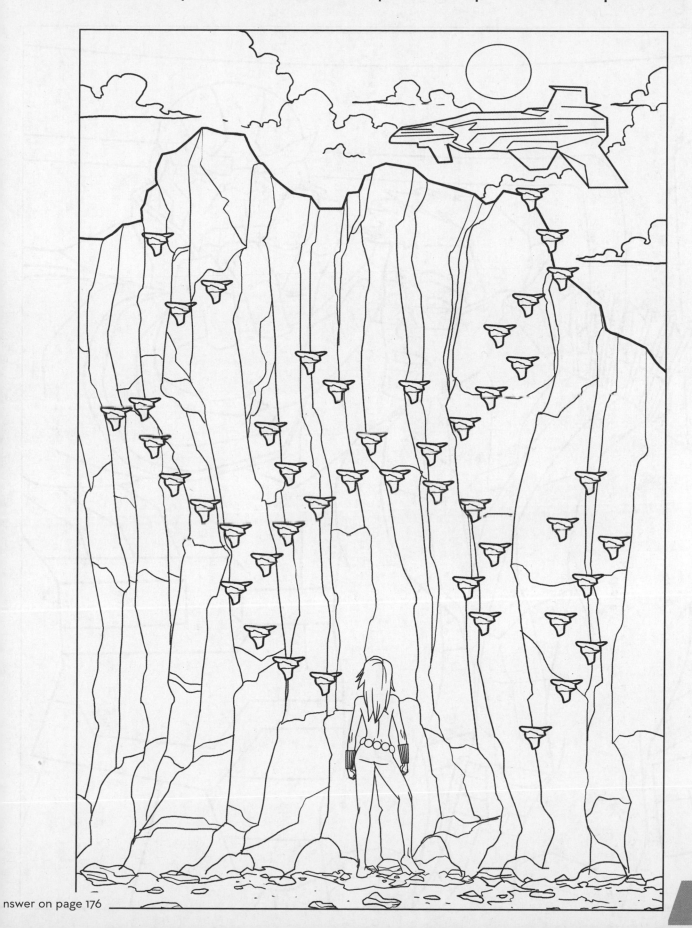

Someone has brainwashed Hawkeye and wants to make him fight the Avengers!

Unscramble the letters to find out who has captured him.

NHTSOA

_____

Help Black Widow follow the right path to find Thanos.

Answer on page 176

Black Widow sneaks up on Thanos. She won't let him use Hawkeye against her friends!

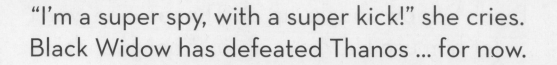

"I'm a super spy, with a super kick!" she cries.
Black Widow has defeated Thanos ... for now.

138

Now Black Widow has to find Hawkeye.
Which door is he trapped behind?

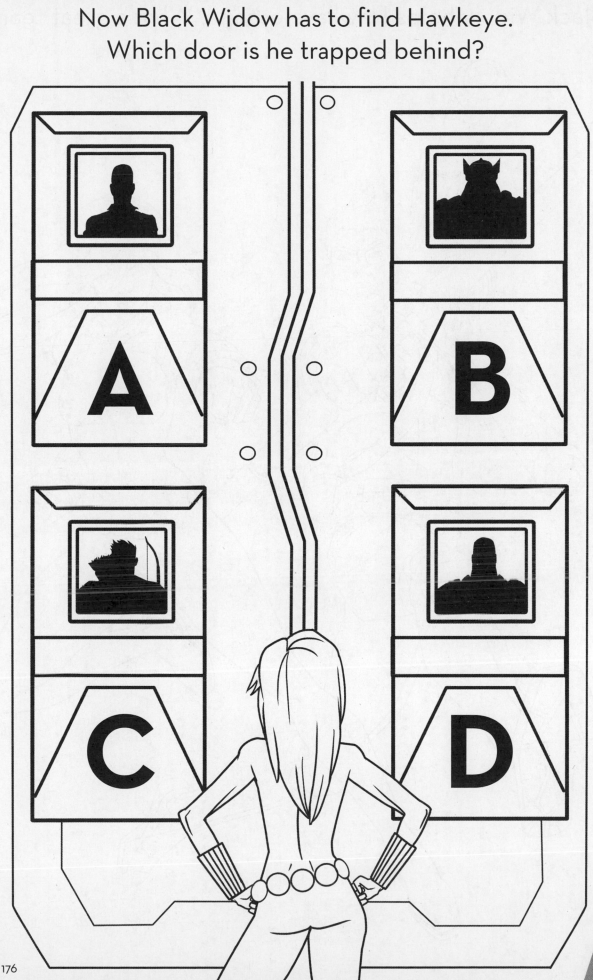

Black Widow helps Hawkeye escape. What a great team!

Colour in these pictures of heroes and villains, then circle the Avengers' enemies.

A. Nick Fury

B. Thanos

C. Loki

D. HYDRA Agent

E. Hulk

F. Abomination

Tony Stark is preparing for a day of crime fighting as Iron Man. Can you help him choose the right suit?

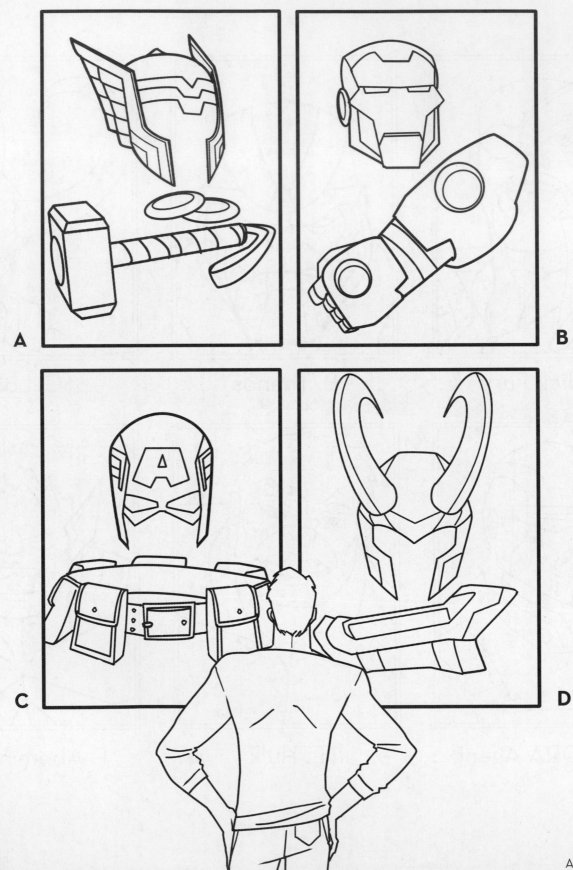

A

B

C

D

Answer on page 176

"Iron Man, we need you back at S.H.I.E.L.D.," says Nick Fury.
"Something's come up."

"Armoured Avenger, reporting for duty."

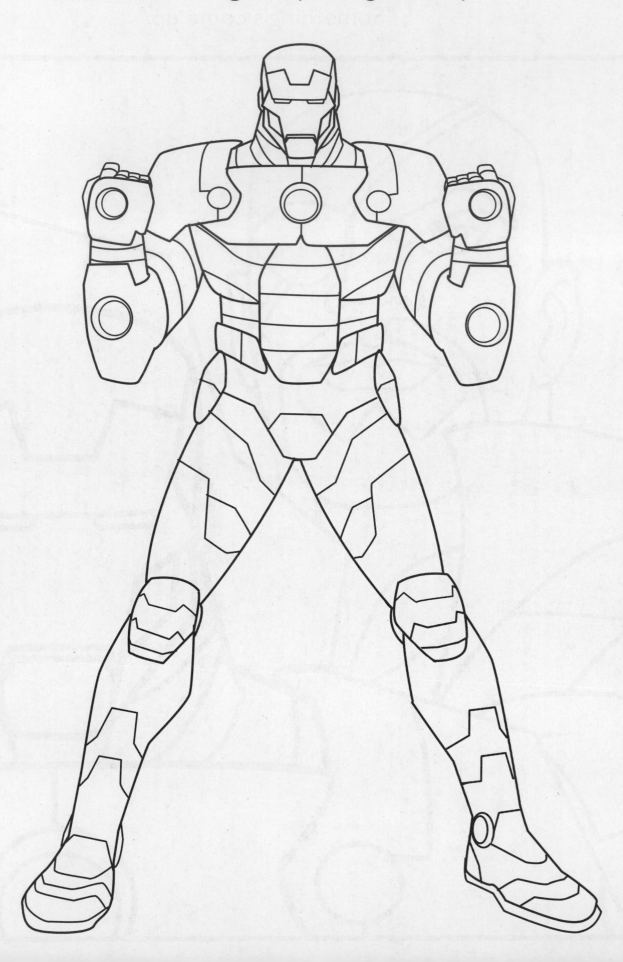

Whiplash is back – and he's improved his whips!
Can you spot five differences between these two pictures?

"Today is not your day, Whiplash!" shouts Iron Man.

Iron Man is here to save the day, but Whiplash won't
go down without a fight. Draw the villain's whips
lashing out at Iron Man!

"You're too slow, Whiplash!" Iron Man teases.

"Sorry about the mess," Iron Man says to the farmer.
Iron Man has won this round. Time to head back to S.H.I.E.L.D.

Falcon and Redwing have been training all day.
"I think that's enough for today," Falcon tells his friend.

"What are you up to, Big Bird?" says Iron Man.

"Why don't you race me to the other side of
the canyon and find out!" replies Falcon.

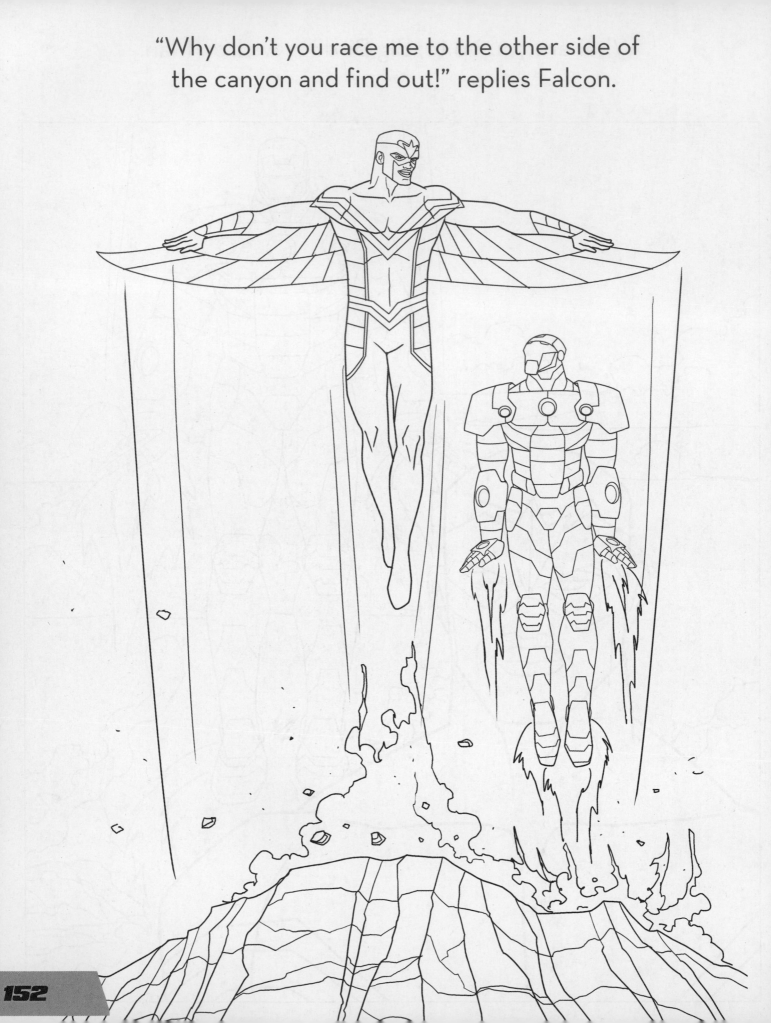

Find a path through the maze to help the heroes race to the finish!

START

FINISH

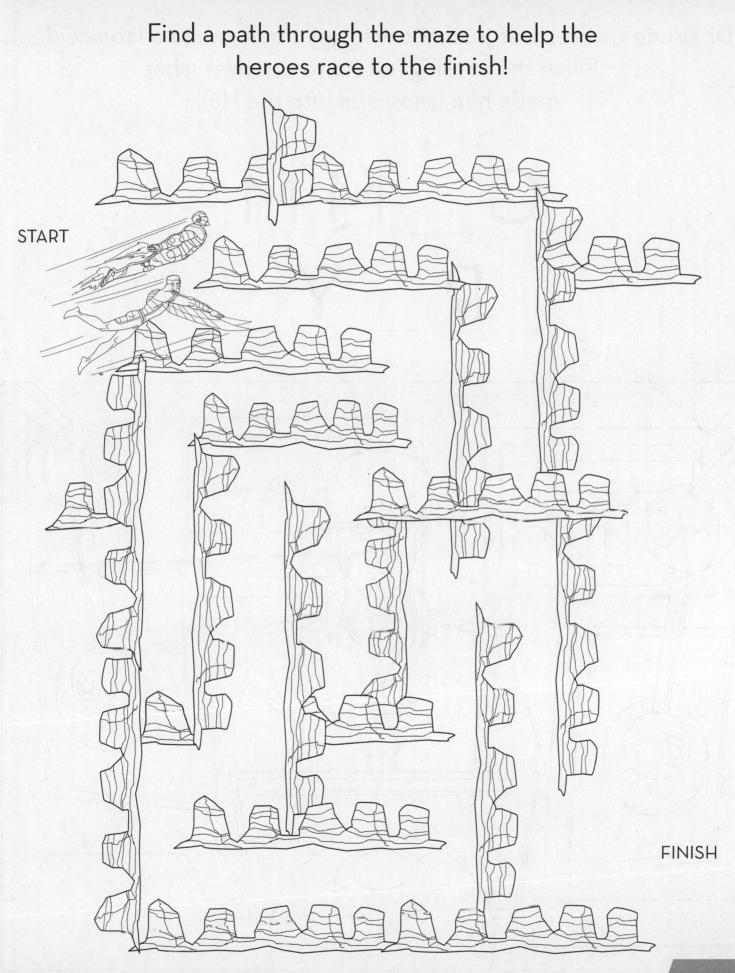

Answer on page 176

Dr Bruce Banner was just a normal guy until he had a lab accident.
Fill in the missing letters to discover what
made him transform into the Hulk!

G _ MM _
R Y _

Answer on page 176

Bruce Banner has to stay calm to avoid turning into the 'other guy'. Circle the thing that is most likely to make him angry.

A

B

C

D

E

Answer on page 176

Thanos is robbing a bank! "This gold will give me everything
I need to match S.H.I.E.L.D.'s resources."

"Knock, knock!" yells the Hulk, as he crashes through a wall. "Hulk smash bad guys!"

"You're too late, Hulk! I have what I came for," growls Thanos.

"Hulk stop Thanos with ... HULK CLAP!"
BOOM!

Thanos's treasure is ruined! Can you put the gold pieces back together again? Draw lines to join the matching pieces.

Answers on page 176

Thanos is no match for the Hulk. Colour in the Jade Giant.

How many of these words can you find in the grid below?
Remember to look up, down, forwards, backwards and diagonally.

HAMMER
SHIELD
ARROW

BOW
FEATHER
BELT

B T C P E S E H
E E O A P H O A S
A S K L R O I A M
F E A T H E R M
N O R M D L X E
A D R A Q D V R
H B O W Y L W C
T R W R O O T I

Answers on page 176

Colour in the Avengers Quinjet.

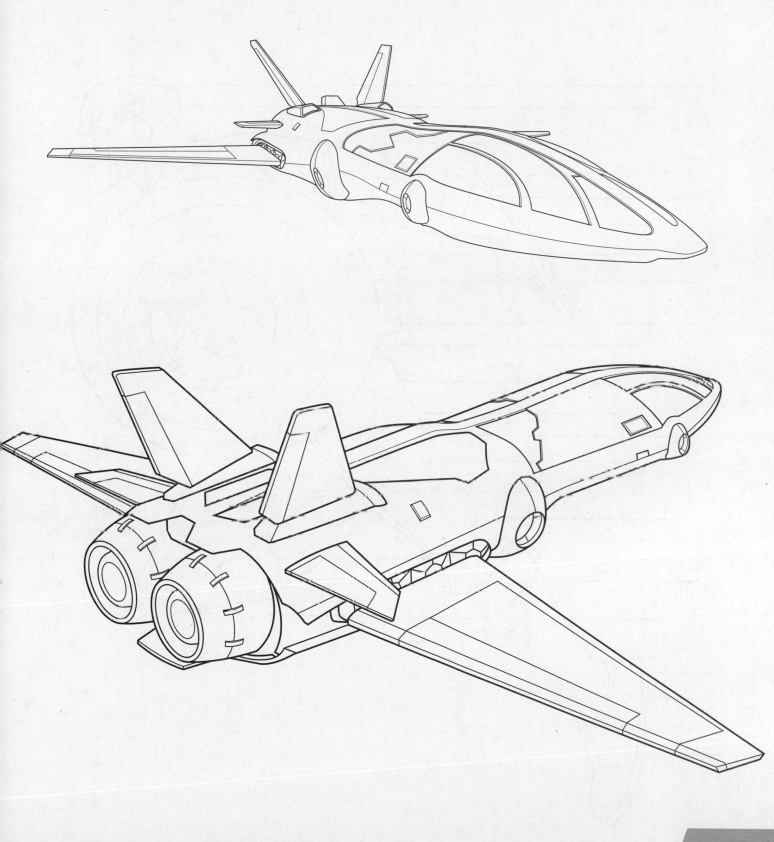

Captain America is ready for action!

"Just another beautiful day in the city. Or is it?"

Uh-oh! Looks like Red Skull is back. Help Captain America find out where the trouble is by leading him through the maze.

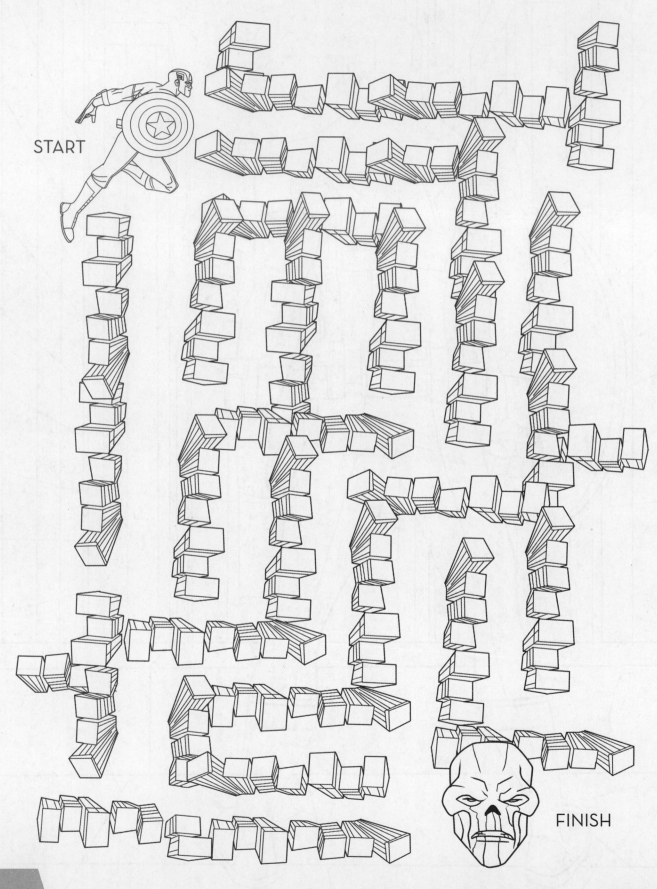

START

FINISH

Answer on page 176

Red Skull is the leader of the evil organization, HYDRA.

"Time to end this, Red Skull!" shouts Captain America.

"You wish, old man!" laughs Red Skull.

Falcon has come to battle Red Skull, too. "Need a hand ... or a wing?" he asks. Join the dots to help Falcon save the day!

"Not today, Red Skull!" yell the Avengers, as they leap into action!

Can you find the symbol that completes Captain America's shield?

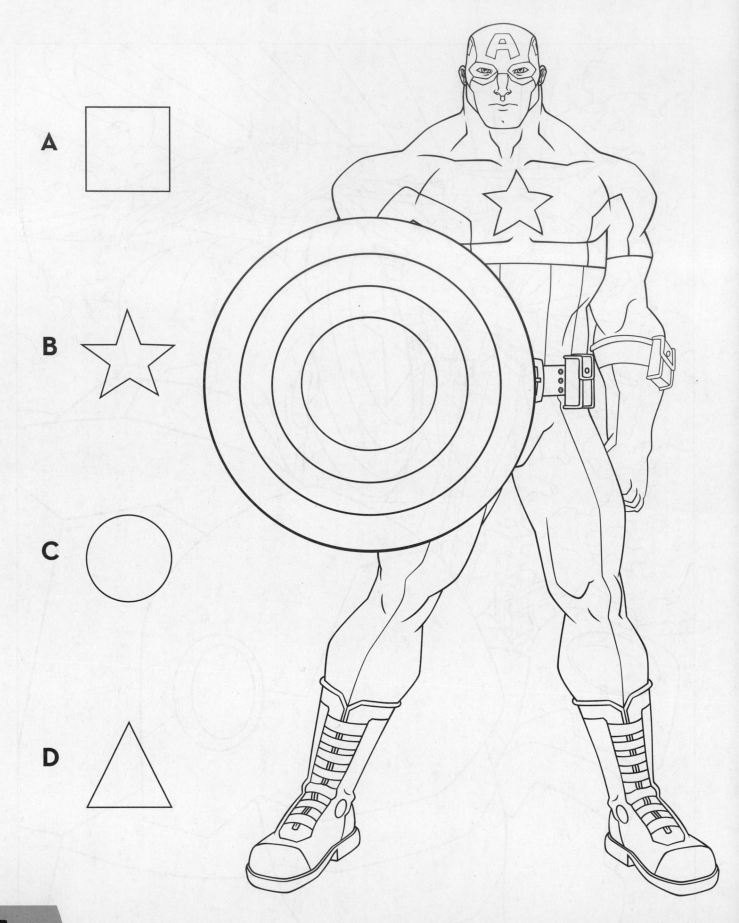

A

B

C

D

Answer on page 176

Defeated! Red Skull is no match for Falcon and Captain America.

At Avengers Tower, Iron Man has spotted something.
"My systems tell me something is heading
towards Earth ... and fast!"

Time to get to work! Fill in the missing letters
to complete the heroes' battle call.

"A_E_GE__, A__E___E!"

Answers

Page 115:
1. LOKI
2. ULTRON
3. THANOS
4. HYDRA
5. RED SKULL

Page 119: C
Page 120: The Hulk
Page 123: Thor
Page 128: E
Page 129: A-2, B-4, C-3, D-5, E-1
Page 130:

Pages 131: C
Page 133:

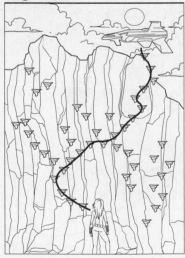

Page 135: THANOS

Page 136:

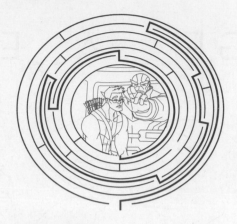

Page 139: C
Page 141: B, C, D and F
Page 142: B
Page 145:

Page 153:

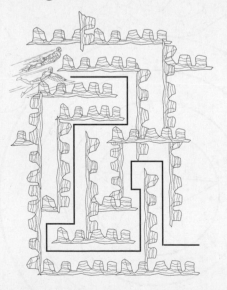

Page 154: GAMMA RAYS
Page 155: D

Page 160:

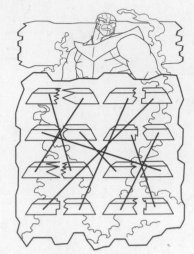

Page 162:

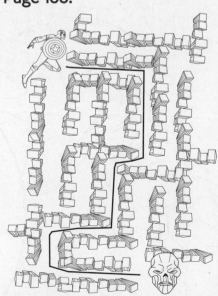

Page 166:

Page 172: B
Page 173:
"AVENGERS, ASSEMBLE!"

A world filled with ideas, hope and potential will always attract a great many villains.

But for every villain that attacks,
there is a hero to defeat them....

Iron Man is known to the world as billionaire
genius Tony Stark. Tony built the suit for himself.
The arc reactor technology within his chest keeps
Tony's injured heart beating and powers the suit.
People say the armour makes him powerful ...
... some might even say invincible.

Tony is not the only Super Hero.

Natasha Romanoff spent years training to be a top secret spy, handling missions some thought to be myth.

Eventually, Natasha was recruited by Nick Fury and S.H.I.E.L.D., where she was given high-tech equipment and the code name 'Black Widow'.

And Black Widow can always rely on Hawkeye.

Orphaned at an early age, Clint Barton worked for a travelling circus as a master archer. After witnessing Iron Man rescue people in danger, Clint knew that he too wanted to be a Super Hero and help those in need.

Clint made a costume and all manner of trick arrows, equipped with exploding tips, stunners and electrical nets. He became known as Hawkeye and joined the mighty Avengers.

And when Hawkeye's arrows aren't enough, there is always ... the Hulk!

After being exposed to gamma radiation, scientist Bruce Banner spent most of his life on the run. He always tried to stay calm because sometimes his emotions could get the better of him....

Banner can transform into a huge green hero, who's always ready to save the day. But no matter how much he tries to help, people find it very hard to trust him. So the Hulk mostly keeps to himself.

Far away, in a place called Asgard, Thor made someone very angry. His brother, Loki, wanted to rule Asgard – or anywhere else for that matter. So Thor imprisoned his brother on a place called the Isle of Silence.

Loki didn't take this well. He wanted revenge!

Loki used his powers to search the Earth – a place his brother loves and has sworn to protect – to find someone people feared. Someone they distrusted. But, above all, someone who could defeat his brother, Thor.

Loki soon found someone – the Incredible Hulk!

The master of mischief, Loki, used his powers to trick the Hulk into thinking a high-speed train was about to crash on a broken train track.

The Hulk stopped the train, thinking he had saved the day.

But the broken track was just an illusion. The people on the train thought the Hulk was trying to hurt them. Word spread fast – the Hulk was on a rampage!

Soon after, the most powerful heroes in the world arrived to save the day.

But Loki had only wanted to lure Thor there, not the others! The Hulk might have been able to crush Thor, but he wouldn't stand a chance against four Super Heroes.

Loki used his powers again to create a version of the Hulk that only Thor could see. Then Loki returned to Asgard, and Thor chased after the fake Hulk!

But when Thor tried to strike the Hulk, his mighty hammer went right through him.

"An illusion!" Thor said – and he knew it could only be the work of Loki. Thor rushed back to Asgard and confronted his brother. Like the true coward he was ... Loki ran.

But Thor grabbed Loki and brought him down to Earth once again. Thor found the other heroes. They had cornered the real Hulk, who still thought he had done something wrong. Thor dropped Loki into the middle of the battle.

"Thou must know – this is your true villain! My brother, Loki of Asgard, tricked you into believing our comrade, the Hulk, smashed the train!"

And with that, Loki used his magic against the heroes. He created multiple illusions of himself. The Avengers didn't know which was the real Loki, so they attacked them all.

But one hero would not be tricked.

The group liked working together. They realized that as individuals, they were just Super Heroes. But as a team, they were a mighty, unstoppable force! So they became ...

the Avengers!

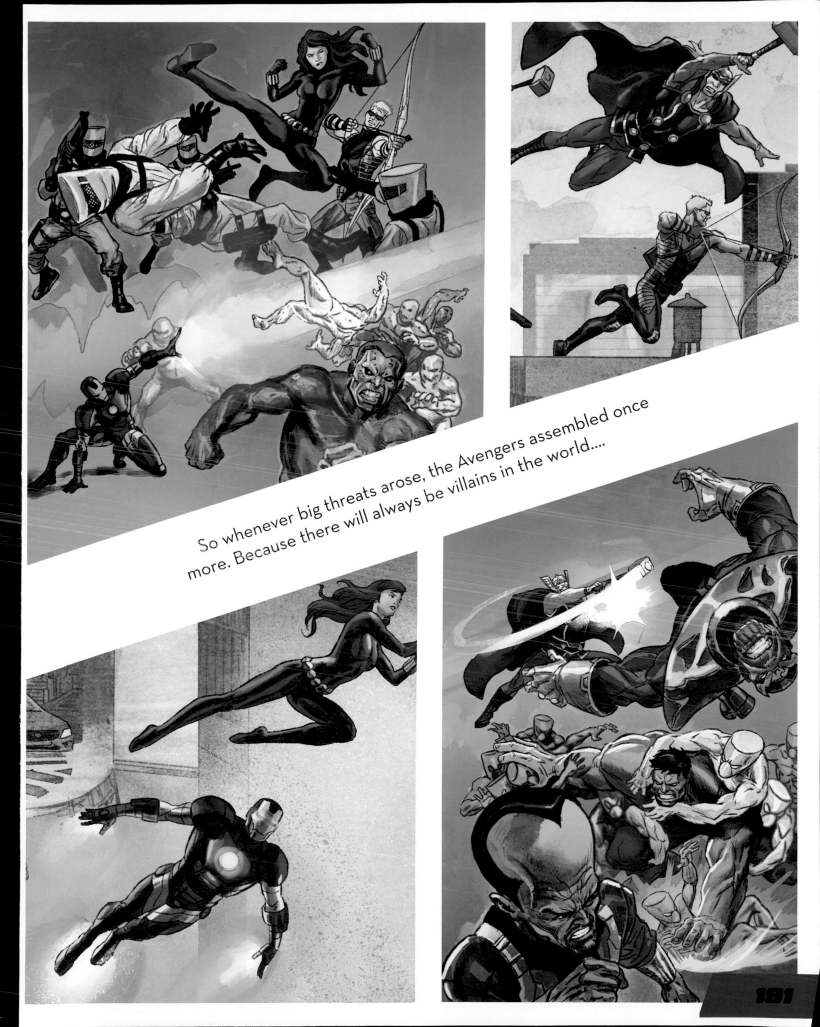

So whenever big threats arose, the Avengers assembled once more. Because there will always be villains in the world....

After completing a mission in the Arctic Circle, where they had battled
Namor, the Prince of Atlantis, the Avengers rode off in their submarine.
    But soon, they spotted something floating in the distance. It looked like
something frozen in a block of ice!
    The Incredible Hulk swam to the figure and took it back to the sub.
He took the block to the medical bay. There was a man trapped inside!

Iron Man slowly thawed the ice, to reveal ...

... Captain America! The famous Super-Soldier from World War II!
Cap had saved the world from the evil organization HYDRA and its leader, Red Skull. But he was trapped in ice and had lain there for decades!
Confused and on guard, Cap listened to the Avengers explain what had happened. They told him they were friends.
But before the group could get too friendly, the sub suddenly shook.

Namor was back and he'd brought an army of Atlanteans with him!
The Avengers fought hard, but they were no match for an entire army. They were overwhelmed.
But then someone who was not an Avenger stepped in ...

... and the tide began to turn! The Avengers, together with Captain America, defeated Namor and his army. They had stopped him from waging war on the surface world.

They were proud of the way they had worked together. The final member of their team was in place. Captain America raised his shield and the others rallied around him.

A new team had been born: Thor, Hulk, Hawkeye, Black Widow, Iron Man ... and now, Captain America!

The world would soon realize this group was something mighty.

And if a threat were ever to arise that was too big for one hero ... the Avengers would assemble!

GUARDIANS OF THE GALAXY

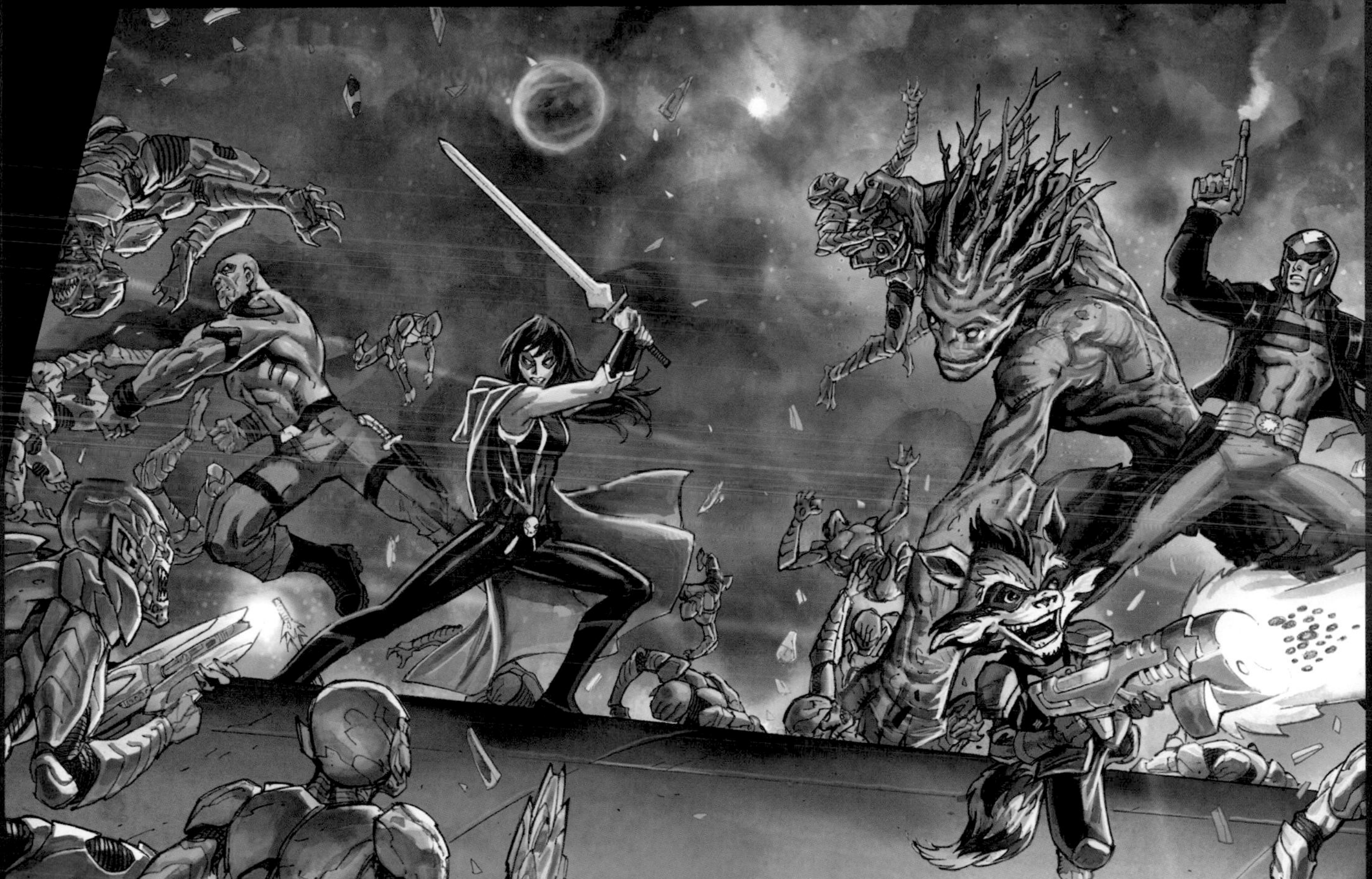

BEGINNINGS

The universe is vast and beautiful, and within it live both good and evil. And sometimes, evil goes looking for a fight.

That's when a group of heroes comes forth to save the day. These heroes are ... the

Guardians of the Galaxy!

Led by Star-Lord, the Guardians of the Galaxy vow to protect those in need. But Star-Lord hasn't always been a hero. His story started on that tiny planet behind him, when he was just a little boy named Peter Quill.

Like most children, Peter played outside and read comic books, and he was fascinated by the stars and the galaxy. He also believed in doing the right thing. Peter stood up for himself and protected others. Even then Peter was a Guardian. And when Peter grew up, he became a Guardian of the Earth as ...

... Star-Lord!

After years of travelling across the galaxy as a carefree space explorer, Peter realized he needed a change. He missed his friends and family – and he knew of the evil in the universe, ready to wipe out his loved ones when it got the chance.

Peter needed to protect his home planet, but he couldn't do it alone.

First he met Gamora.

With her people enslaved and her village destroyed by the Badoon – a warlike empire intent on destroying all things good, including Earth – young Gamora fled her planet. She was very young and very scared.

Taken in by Thanos, the most feared villain in the universe, Gamora was raised to be a dangerous warrior.

But after many years, Gamora realized Thanos was just like the Badoon, so she fled once again, vowing always to fight evil.

Gamora agreed to join Star-Lord.

Star-Lord and Gamora met a great warrior named Drax the Destroyer!
Legend had it that Drax had become so enraged when he lost his family to the Badoon, that he defeated one of their fighter ships all by himself!
Since then, Drax had travelled the galaxy, fighting for good, living by his own moral code and desiring peace for everyone.
Knowing what it was like to lose a family, as both Star-Lord and Gamora had, Drax agreed to join their team.

Far away, in another part of the universe, there was Planet X:
a beautiful world filled with sprawling forests and tree-like beings
who had the ability to grow larger, or regrow from a single leaf.
They studied humans and their environment.

One being in particular wanted to know more about the human race.
His name was Groot. Although his speech was limited, it was clear when
Star-Lord met Groot that he had decided to join the quest.

The final member of the team was the one called Rocket Raccoon.
But he was no ordinary raccoon. He was born a fierce fighter on the
planet known as Halfworld. Scientists noticed Rocket and gave him
advanced skills. He learned to use his new talents to do what he loved
most: making new weapons! And firing them at bad guys was his speciality!
So Rocket also joined Star-Lord and his team.

Word of this new alliance travelled fast in space, and it didn't take long for the Badoon to learn of Peter's plan to protect Earth.

So the team of misfits and outlaws quickly suited up ...

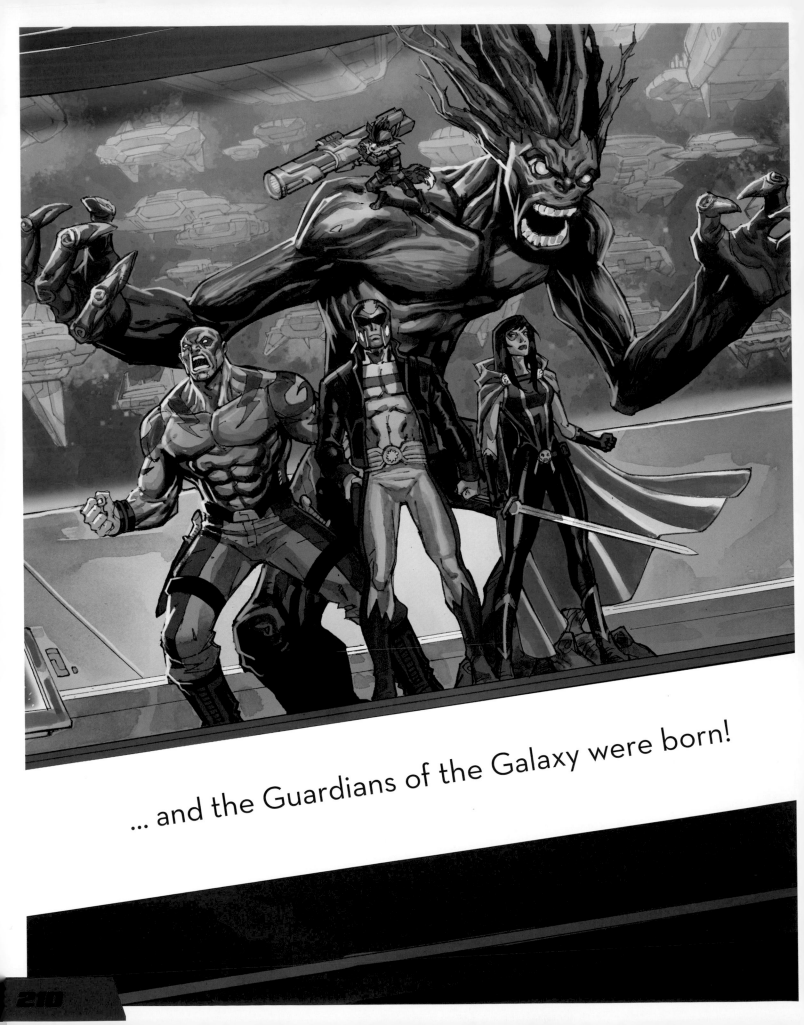

... and the Guardians of the Galaxy were born!

Rocket was the brains of the operation. He helped the Guardians out of seemingly hopeless situations.

Groot's ability to change in size and regrow when injured made him a trusted ally. But he also had heart, which could be useful, too.

Drax's strength – and reputation as the Destroyer – made him a force to be reckoned with.

Gamora's warrior training, combined with her vast knowledge of the galaxy, was invaluable to the Guardians.

Star-Lord had found his team to help him protect Earth. They trusted him and followed his lead across the galaxy.

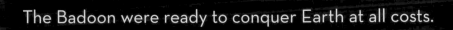

But the Guardians were ready as well!

The Guardians fought with heart, battling long and hard.

Gamora, Drax and Star-Lord worked as a team and tore through the Badoon with ease. Groot grew and grew, towering over the Badoon, while Rocket used his arsenal of weapons to blast at the invading aliens.

And when one needed help, another stepped up to lend a hand!

The battle raged on, until finally ...

... the Guardians defeated the Badoon! Any that had survived quickly retreated to the farthest reaches of the galaxy.

Peter knew stopping the Badoon was a symbol of hope – for the galaxy, for Earth, for his friends and family.

Peter dreamed that, one day, the entire galaxy would be free from evil.
Gamora, Drax, Rocket and Groot – they too shared Peter's dream.

And from that day forward, those who fought against peace would answer to ... the Guardians of the Galaxy!